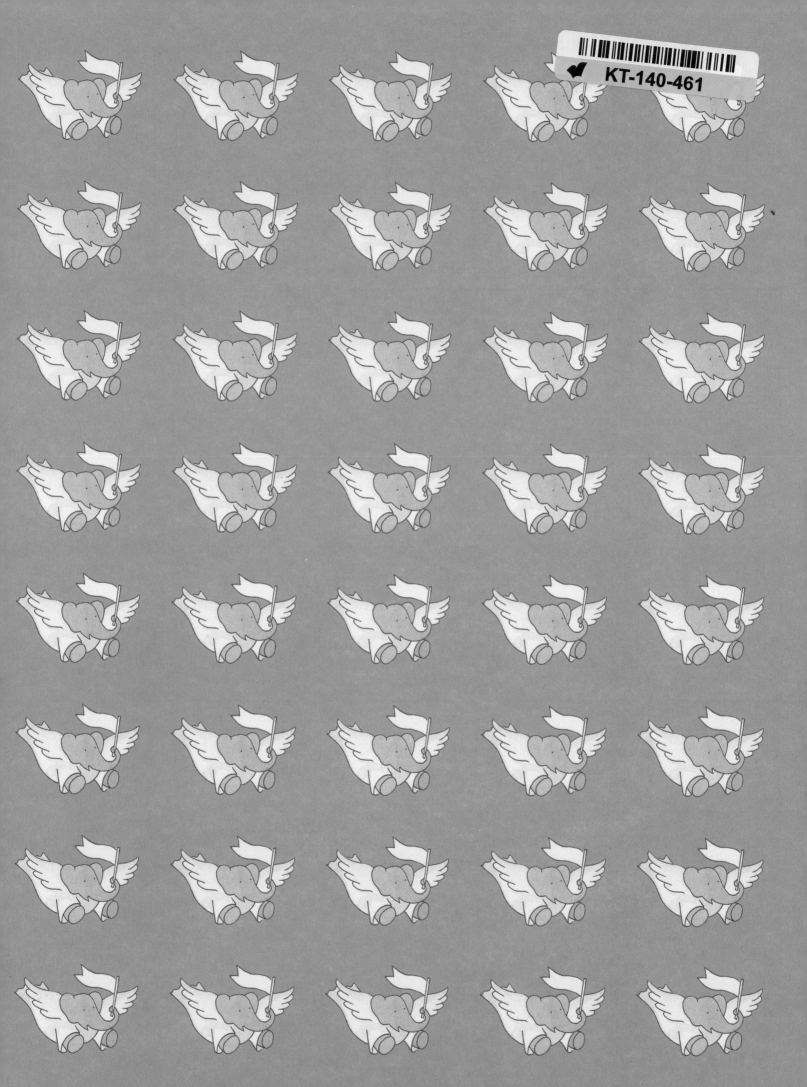

THE WORLD OF

BABAR™

Written by Lesley Young
with illustrations by Ley Roberts

MADCAP

Other Babar titles from Madcap Books include
The Big Bike Race
The Missing Crown
The Race to the Moon

This work conceived, produced and originally published in 1998 by
Madcap Books, André Deutsch Ltd, 76 Dean Street, London, W1V 5HA
André Deutsch is a subsidiary of VCI plc
www.vci.co.uk

Babar characters™ and © 1998 Laurent de Brunhoff
Licensed by Nelvana Limited and The Clifford Ross Company Ltd.
Adapted by Lesley Young and Ley Honor Roberts, based on characters created by
Jean and Laurent de Brunhoff

Design by Robert Kelland

Origination by Digicol, London

A catalogue record for this title is available from the British Library

ISBN 0 233 99395 9

Printed in Italy

Babar Says, **'Take Care!'** In this book there are lots of wonderful things to do and make. When you are cooking or using scissors, always ask an adult to help you.

CONTENTS

CATCH ME

The jungle is a great place for games.
Here are some of Babar and his
family and friends' favourites.

SHIPWRECK

For three or more players. Set up lots of 'islands' – logs, old tyres, rugs, upturned buckets –
even sheets of newspaper. Whoever is 'it' tries to catch the others, but they are safe if they
are on an island. No one can stay on an island for longer than ten seconds.

FREEZE TAG

For four or more players. Whoever is 'it'
runs around trying to touch other players. Anyone touched must
freeze on the spot. Another player can set the frozen player free
by touching him or her – they can then start running around
again. The first to be frozen three times becomes the next 'it'.

4

IF YOU CAN

You have probably played tag.
These are different versions
which make it more fun:

CHAIN TAG

This is a good game for six or more players. One person is 'it'.
When he or she catches someone, they have to join hands and try to catch the others
together. The last person to be caught is the winner.

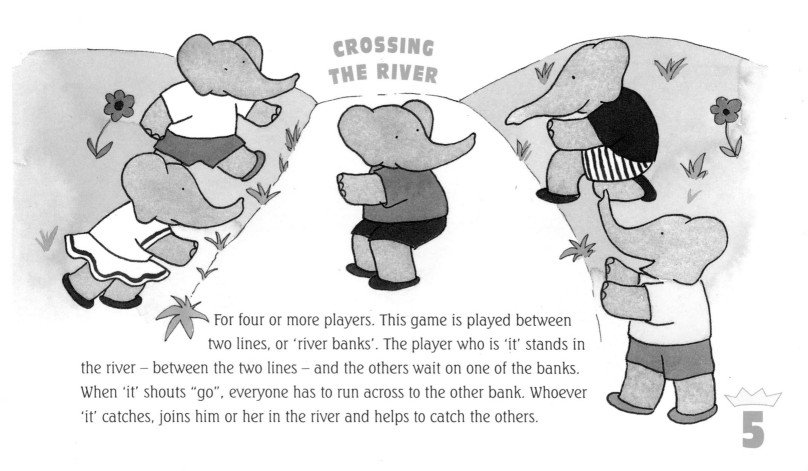

CROSSING THE RIVER

For four or more players. This game is played between
two lines, or 'river banks'. The player who is 'it' stands in
the river – between the two lines – and the others wait on one of the banks.
When 'it' shouts "go", everyone has to run across to the other bank. Whoever
'it' catches, joins him or her in the river and helps to catch the others.

RACING

SEDAN CHAIR

This is Flora's favourite game. It is good for a party, because you need quite a few players. Two players link hands and form a seat. A third player sits in the seat and each group of three run towards the finish. Of course, Flora and Isabelle use their trunks.

SACK RACE

Dustbin liners make good sacks. (Remember to take the rubbish out first!)

WHEELBARROW

For pairs. One player holds the legs of another, who moves forwards by using his hands to cover the ground.

GAMES

THREE-LEGGED RACE

Run in pairs, inside legs tied together
(old tights cut in two are good to use as ties).
In Celesteville, the flamingoes usually win
this one – not because of their long legs,
but, near the end, they take off and soar
over the finishing line, wings flapping.

 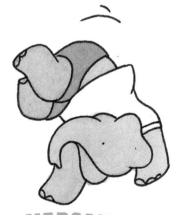 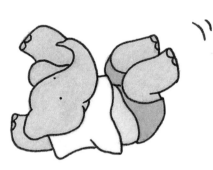

SOMERSAULTS

Each player moves forward as fast as possible in a series of somersaults.

KANGAROO

Each player has something between their knees,
so has to jump forwards. If coconuts are not
handy, use balloons, grapefruits – or balls
of scrunched-up paper.

BABAR'S

Babar loves being a father. His children remind him of his early life in the jungle with his own mother. Like all elephants, Babar never forgets. Here are pictures of three of his children – Pom, Flora and Alexander. Trace round the pictures, copy on to white card and cut out.

ALEXANDER

CHILDREN

There are also some clothes to dress your figures in.
Trace round them, and copy on to white paper or
thin card. Cut out, cutting carefully round the tabs.
Now colour in the clothes with felt-tip pens or paint.
Copy the designs shown here, or add some new ones
of your own. Dress your figures by folding
the tabs on the clothes back over them.

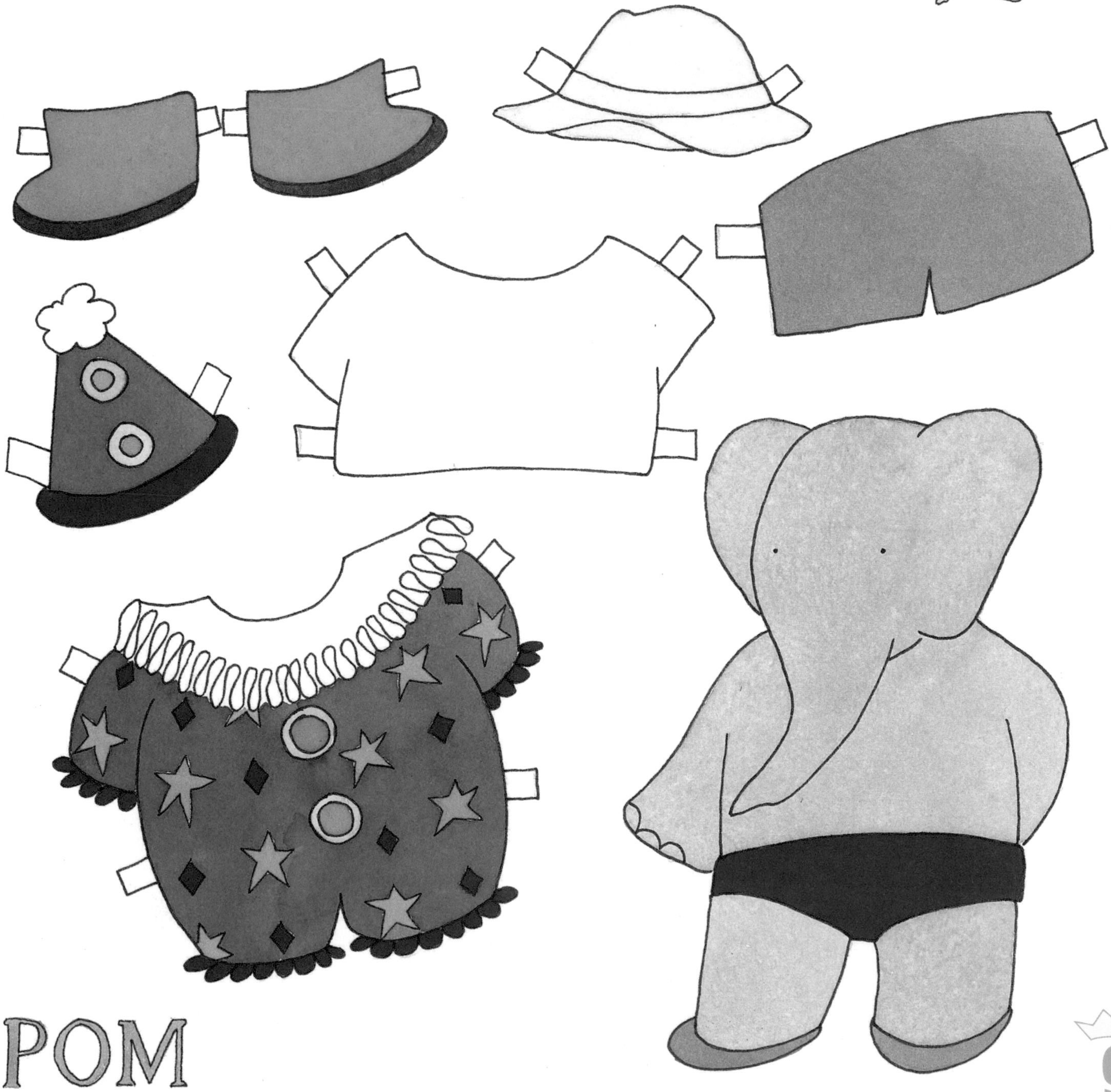

POM

FLORA

Use a dough to make more elephant figures. You will need: 2 cups flour, ½ cup salt, water.

Mix the flour and salt together in a bowl. Slowly add about ¾ cup of water and mix with a spoon. Finally, knead the mixture together with your hands until the dough is firm but not dry.

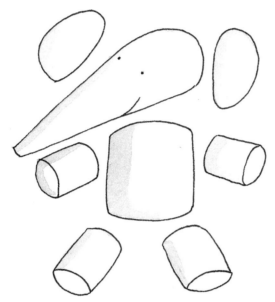

Shape the dough into body parts. Then stick all the body parts together and place on a baking tray.

Bake the model elephants at gas mark 4 (180°C) for ten to fifteen minutes, until hard. Paint the figures with acrylic paint. Varnish with clear varnish for a super-shiny finish.

Elephant models make lovely gifts. Small ones like these, with ribbon glued or taped to their backs, make wonderful Christmas decorations. You could have your own Babar Christmas tree!

BABAR'S

COCO

Coco is the clown of Celesteville. Babar decided it was just as important to have a clown as it was to have gardeners and cleaners. Coco makes sure that all his subjects are kept happy and smiling!

Barbacol is the tailor. But no matter how many suits Babarcol makes, none please Babar as much as the very first green suit the Old Lady gave him. When he went back to the jungle and took off his jacket, the elephants were amazed – they thought he was shedding his skin, like a snake!

BARBACOL

FRIENDS

Justinen is the painter. He paints portraits of the elephants and captures the bright blue of the lake and the zingy colours of all the jungle plants.

The Old Lady met Babar when he ran away from the jungle. She showed him how to live in a big town, but now she lives in Celesteville. She is the special friend of King Babar.

13

ARTHUR

Arthur is Celeste's younger brother and Babar's cousin. He enjoys leading Flora, Pom and Alexander into mischief.

Celesteville wouldn't be the same without Zephir's monkey business. He swings through the trees, as fast as the wind, swooping down now and then to perform a trick and make everyone laugh.

ZEPHIR

14

FRIENDS

Cornelius is the oldest and wisest of all the elephants. Babar always listens carefully to what he says. One of his best decisions was that Babar should be king of the elephants. He told him that the jungle was changing and they must all change with it, and he has helped Babar every step of the way.

Dr Capoulosse looks after the health of all the elephants – whether they have been bitten by a snake or have eaten too many green bananas.

GROW YOUR

Transform a patch of garden

SUNFLOWERS

1 Sunflowers are best planted against a wall or fence, in a sunny, sheltered place. Sow the seeds in the spring in groups of three, 40 centimetres (15 inches) apart.

3 When the plants have grown up a bit, tie them to canes driven into the soil beside them for support. They should grow to a jungle size of three to four metres (10 – 13 feet) or more.

MARROWS

Sow marrow seeds and, when the vegetables appear, carve a name by cutting away some of the skin. As they grow, so will the name. Carve a friend's name, and give the fully grown name as a present.

BABAR

OWN JUNGLE

into your own piece of jungle.

When the plants appear, weed out two of every three seedlings, leaving the strongest.

2 Water the plants often – especially in dry weather, adding liquid feed to the water to make them grow tall.

4 When the flowers die, you can roast the seeds in the oven and eat them, or save them and plant them next year. More jungle plants to try: pampas grass; quaking grass; red hot pokers.

GOURDS

These come in all shapes and sizes, plain and striped. Buy a packet of mixed seeds and sow them. Water and feed them. When they are fully grown, bring them inside to dry. The seeds inside them rattle about: two matching gourds make good maracas. Varnish them to preserve them.

This is a picture of Babar, in the new green suit which the Old Lady bought him.

It is great fun to take your own photographs, as Flora discovered when she was given a camera for her birthday. It took her some time to get the hang of it, but if you look at her first efforts, you can learn from her mistakes.

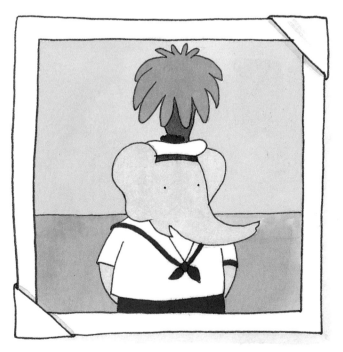

Arthur has a palm tree growing out of his head. Flora should have asked him to move to one side a bit, then we would have seen them both properly.

18

A wonderful picture of Zephir's tail. This was meant to be an action shot of him swinging through the trees. But Flora was too slow!

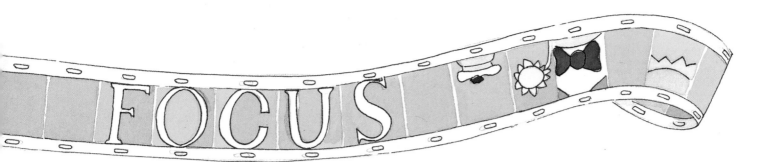

Celeste in her best dress. Night falls fast in the jungle – but not that fast. Flora forgot to take the cover off her camera lens.

Alexander enjoying an ice cream. He seems to have a tiny head and huge feet, as Flora held the camera much too near the ground.

Pom is trembling as if he's being charged by a herd of rhinos. Flora moved as she took the picture, making it look as if Pom's shaking.

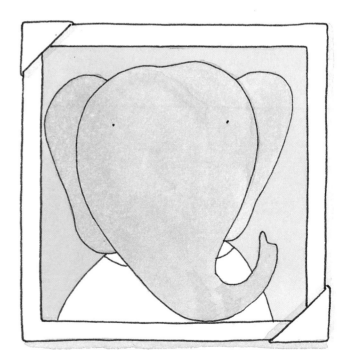

No, Alexander hasn't been stung by a swarm of bees. Flora held her camera much too close to his face, making it look as if it's all swollen.

MONKEY

Zephir loves getting up to mischief and making people laugh. He has brought lots of fun into the Old Lady's life. Here are two tricks he performed for her birthday. Try them and amaze your friends!

PUTTING AN ELEPHANT THROUGH A POSTCARD

Zephir holds a postcard up in front of his audience and says he's going to cut a hole in it big enough for Pom to pass through. It sounds impossible. The trick is in the way he cuts the hole.

WHAT TO DO:

First, fold the card in half lengthways as shown.

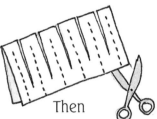

Next, take a pair of scissors and make a series of cuts from the fold outwards, stopping short of the outer edge.

Then make cuts between the first ones, starting from the outer edge and stopping short of the fold.

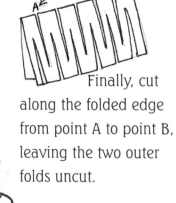

Finally, cut along the folded edge from point A to point B, leaving the two outer folds uncut.

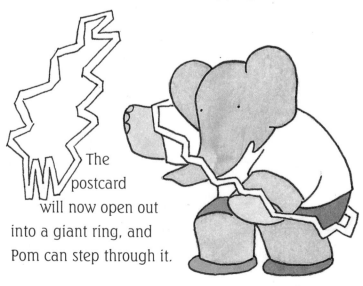

The postcard will now open out into a giant ring, and Pom can step through it.

BUSINESS

THE PAPER BAG TRICK

YOU WILL NEED:

Two paper bags the same size and colour. Coloured paper. Some white tissues. Scissors. Glue.

Cut about 1 cm (½ inch) off the top of one bag.

Cut some holes in the bottom of the bag, to let air through when you blow into it

Cut the coloured paper into tiny bits, like confetti.

Put the bits into the second bag.

Glue the edges of the two bags together round the tops.

WHAT TO DO:

Show the audience the bag. 'This is an ordinary bag, empty, as you can see.' Put the tissues in the bag – 'I put the tissues in the bag.' Blow up the bag and say, 'I will now blow up the bag and say the magic word – Zephir!' Burst the bag, then quickly crumple it and throw it away. 'The tissues have turned to confetti!'

21

JUNGLE

News in Celesteville is spread by all the animals – especially the chattering monkeys – but everyone also likes to read the 'Jungle Times'.

JUNGLE TIMES

ISSUE Nº 1   SATURDAY   WHAT TO PUT IN...

News Reports

Write about anything interesting that has happened in your area, especially anything funny or unusual. Ask friends and neighbours for ideas. Report

First prizewinner in the Celesteville skating competition glides to victory.

Features

Ask someone to write about something that really interests them – beekeeping, pop music, ghosts – and then edit to make it as exciting as possible for the reader.

A gallant loser in the skating final tests the ice for strength.

on parties, outings or school trips.

Above: Palace news flash: dented crown.

NEWS

Make your own newspaper. Do it by yourself – or divide up the tasks among a group of friends. It can be put together in a day, with other issues to follow, or spread over a holiday.

What to put in:

Interviews

Choose someone to interview and decide what to ask them. Interview a friend or relative about a special interest. An old relative could tell you about their childhood memories – how they celebrated Christmas, or a trip to the seaside. Arrange an appointment first, and never interview a stranger alone. Plan your questions in advance and take a notebook or a tape recorder.

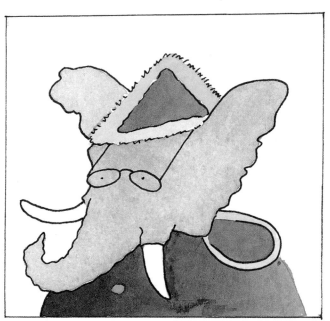

CORNELIUS: *"I remember when that palm tree was just a coconut…"*

Advertisements

10ᴾ OFF YOUR NEXT ISSUE OF JUNGLE NEWS

Ask friends and family if they have anything they would like to swap. Advertise lost pets or possessions. Offer services like dog-walking or shopping.

Watering a garden when the owner is on holiday is always popular.

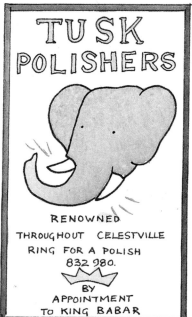

TUSK POLISHERS

RENOWNED THROUGHOUT CELESTVILLE RING FOR A POLISH 832 980.

BY APPOINTMENT TO KING BABAR

LOST !! ZEPHIRS HAT last seen on his head REWARD OF 20 BANANAS PLEASE RING THE PALACE WITH ANY IMFORMATION.

SWAPS **De luxe deckchair** *offered as swap for large bottle of calamine lotion.*
Three small dresses *offered as swap for exercise bike…*

FOUND **Tame canary.** *Answers to name of Joe. Also answers to Harry or Alexander. In fact, answers to any name…*
WANTED **Old lemonade bottles.** *Every donor will receive bottle of home-made ginger beer in a few weeks' time.*

23

Reviews

Write – or ask someone to write about – books, plays, television programmes or videos. Good reviews can be of things you hated as well as those you loved. Review local restaurants or cafés. Do a survey of all the pizza places in your area.

The Old Lady reviews the jungle smash hit, 'Swan Lake':

Flora reaches for the stars and pirouettes to fame in 'Swan Lake'.

This was a magical show! The high point came when the flamingos flew overhead and dropped showers of orange petals. Skilful lighting – wired in the trees by Zephir – highlighted the dazzling young dancers. Flora's leaps brought cheers from the audience. A star is born!

Recipes

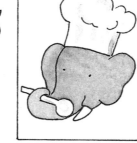

Ask the best cook you know for some ideas. Share recipes which include a secret, delicious and easy-to-make banana cake.

Grease a 20.5cm (8") round cake tin and line the base with greased greaseproof paper. Sift 175g (6oz) self-raising flour, ¼ level tsp baking powder and ¼ level tsp bicarbonate of soda into a bowl. Rub in 50g (2oz) butter with your fingertips and stir in 150g (5oz) caster sugar.

Peel and mash 175g (6oz) ripe bananas in a bowl and add 3 tbsps milk and 1 beaten egg. Stir this into the dry ingredients, put in tin and bake (180°C 350°F) for about 40 minutes. Allow cake to cool, cut in half and fill with chilled cream cheese mixed with 1 chopped banana and a little brown sugar.

CROSSWORD

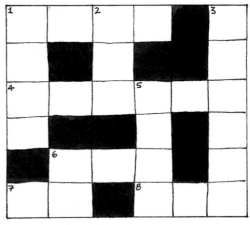

These are as much fun to make up as they are to do. Trace this crossword and fit words into the grid. You can make up the clues afterwards.

Competitions

Ask for entrants to a tennis tournament or a pancake-tossing competition. Who can grow the tallest sunflower, or make the best Christmas decoration?

Set a topic for a picture, ('My favourite thing...'). They can be painted or photographed. Arrange an exhibition of all the pictures and appoint a judge.

Copy out the twelve signs of the zodiac from a newspaper and write a prediction for each one. Examples below:

• Libra •
A far-flung relative has very good news and is waiting to hear from you, so make that trunk-call now!

• Scorpio •
This is a boomerang week – whatever you give out will come back to you, so make sure it's good.

• Pisces •
Be on the lookout for an exciting surprise. A good time to clean your windows.

• Gemini •
Someone is going to tell you a secret. For goodness sake, keep it under your hat!

• Capricorn •
Life seems very serious. But cheer up – you are about to come across some jokes that will make you laugh…

SPORT

Include funny or unusual 'sports' like tiddleywinks or blow-football.

JOKES AND COMIC STRIPS

These are useful to break up pages. Put in your old favourites: 'Why were the Dark Ages so called? *Because there were so many knights about…*'

Why couldn't the elephants go swimming together?
Because they only had one pair of trunks between them.

What's white, fluffy and swings through the trees?
A meringue-utang.

Why is Europe like a frying pan?
Because it has Greece at the bottom.

Who are the strongest workers?

Photographers, because they're always developing.

Copy the style of a strip from a comic and invent your own characters. Or put in people you know (teachers, parents, friends…)

CELESTEVILLE

Babar decided to build Celesteville on the shores of the great lake...

So that the elephants could see the beautiful countryside every day when they woke up. The elephants work in the mornings and play in the afternoons.

Many of the creatures who live in the
they blend into the background, so tha
How many creatures

28

jungle use camouflage – that is,
hey are hidden from their enemies.
can you spot?

29

"Now, until the break of day,

The thing the elephants enjoy most is going to the theatre.

Through this house each fairy stray..."

Here they are, watching one of their favourite plays, 'A Midsummer Night's Dream'.

31

JUNGLE

It is Pom, Alexander and Flora's birthday and Babar and Celeste

Ginger grows wild in the jungle, but, for an endless supply of ginger beer, you can

GROW YOUR OWN GINGER BEER

STARTING THE PLANT

You will need:

50g (2oz) fresh baker's yeast

2 level tbsps caster sugar
2 level tbsps ground ginger
275ml (½ pint) water

Mix the yeast and sugar until they form a liquid. Add the ginger and water and stir well. Pour into a jar and put the lid on.

FEEDING THE PLANT

Add 1 level tsp ground ginger and 1 level tsp caster sugar and stir well. Do this every day for ten days. After ten days, mix 450g (18oz) caster sugar with 825ml (1½ pints water) and bring to the boil, stirring. Cool a little and add the juice of two lemons. Strain this mixture through some fine muslin and add to your plant. Finally, add 3 litres (6 pints) of water and stir well.

BOTTLING

Pour the liquid into bottles (a funnel helps), leaving a space at the top of the bottles. Screw the lids on tightly. Decorate plain gummed labels, add the date, and stick on. Store in a cool place and keep for ten days before drinking.

TO MAKE MORE

Halve the plant (the mixture left in the muslin) and put in two separate jars.
Add 275ml (½ pint) water, 2 level tsps ground ginger and 2 level tsps caster sugar to each jar and stir. The plants are then ready to be fed each day for ten days, as before.

BIRTHDAY PARTY

throw a party to celebrate. Perhaps you would like to try some of their ideas for a party of your own.

CELESTE'S SPECIAL FIZZY JELLIES

Make these with lemonade – or any other fizzy drink. For each 550ml (1 pint) of liquid, you need 10g (½ oz) gelatine. Sprinkle the gelatine into a cup containing 3-4 tbsps of lemonade. Stir, and when the gelatine has soaked up the liquid, put the cup in a pan of barely simmering water and leave until it has dissolved and is transparent. Add the liquid to the rest of the pint of lemonade, stir, and put in the fridge to set. Make the jellies in individual glasses or a large bowl. Celeste has made it in a large clear glass bowl, adding a few drops of blue food colouring and some jelly fish!

CHOCOLATE MARSHMALLOW DIP

Melt a 100g (4oz) bar of plain chocolate, broken into pieces, with 4 tsps of warm milk in a bowl over a pan of hot water. Stir the melted chocolate and stand it on a tray or large plate. Pile pink and white marshmallows round the bowl and give everyone cocktail sticks, to dip the marshmallows in the melted chocolate.

RAINBOW POPCORN

Buy some popping corn and pop it according to the instructions. Paint it with colourful vegetable dyes – you can thread it on to cotton to make garlands for your guests.

When everyone is happily full of food, Babar suggests a treasure hunt. Players follow a series of clues, leading them to the prize or treasure.

BALLOON CLUE
Blow up a balloon and write the clue on it in felt-tip pen. When the writing is dry, let the balloon down.

INVISIBLE CLUE
Write the clue in lemon juice. The paper has to be heated gently for the words to appear.

BABAR'S TREASURE HUNT

You should think up the clues in advance.
Here are some of his ideas:

LIPSTICK CLUE
Write a clue in lipstick
on a window or mirror.

JIGSAW CLUE
Write the clue in bold
letters on a piece of card.
Cut it up into
a few pieces and put it
into an envelope.

TELEPHONE CLUE
The clue is a telephone number
and a password. Tell a friend
to read out the next clue when
they are telephoned.

BABAR PACKS

Babar has always loved travelling – on the ground in his car, or above it, on a huge ship, on skis, and in a cable car.

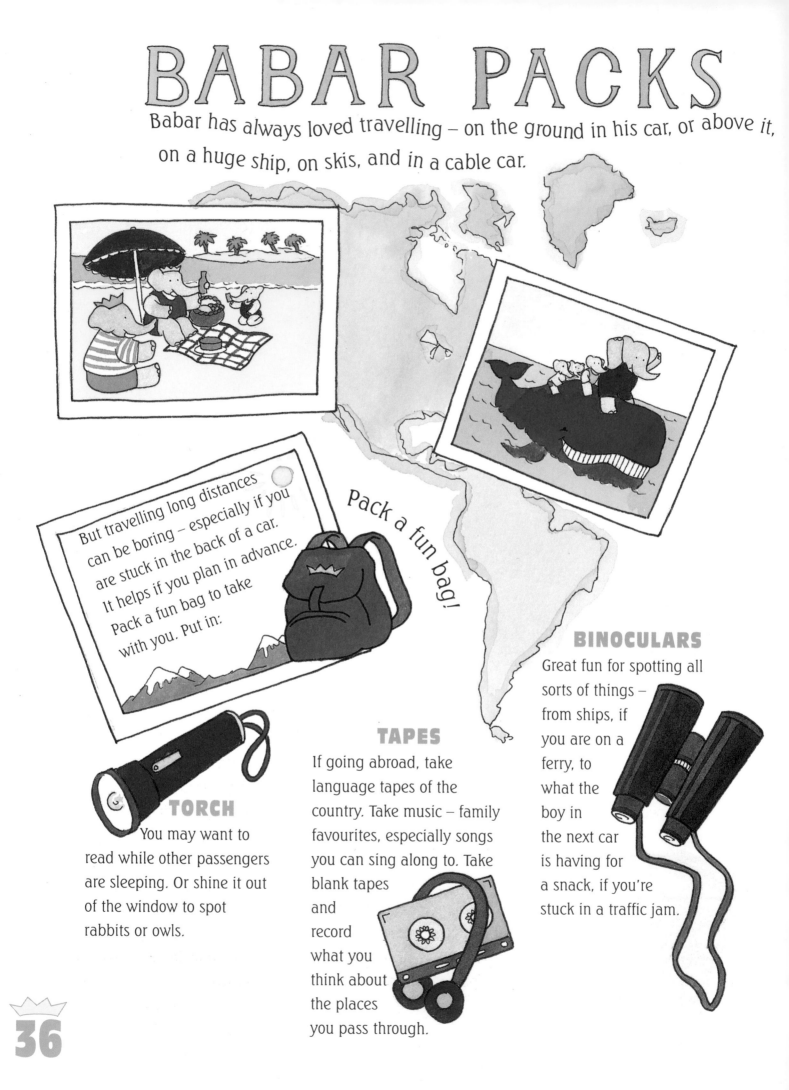

But travelling long distances can be boring – especially if you are stuck in the back of a car. It helps if you plan in advance. Pack a fun bag to take with you. Put in:

Pack a fun bag!

TORCH
You may want to read while other passengers are sleeping. Or shine it out of the window to spot rabbits or owls.

TAPES
If going abroad, take language tapes of the country. Take music – family favourites, especially songs you can sing along to. Take blank tapes and record what you think about the places you pass through.

BINOCULARS
Great fun for spotting all sorts of things – from ships, if you are on a ferry, to what the boy in the next car is having for a snack, if you're stuck in a traffic jam.

HIS TRUNK

in his hot air balloon. He has travelled on the back of a whale,

CALCULATOR

In a car, use this to convert miles to kilometres and gallons to litres. Work out your speed (distance divided by time). Find out the exchange rate and work out how much your lunch cost.

BUBBLES

Not only for tiny children, these are great fun blown from the deck of a ship or an open-top bus when sightseeing. And they cheer up all your fellow passengers too!

NOTEBOOK AND PENS

Keep a log of your journey, writing about the weather, the places that you visit and any sights of special interest. Or keep your log by speaking into a tape recorder and write it up later. Illustrate it with drawings, pressed flowers or leaves, photographs, menus, and postcards.

TRAVEL

NUMBERPLATE GAMES

Numberplate games are always good fun.
Fit letters round the letters of a numberplate,
keeping them in the same order, to make a
new word, for example: FAO – FLAMINGO;
RAX – RATAXES.

Make up phrases using the letters of a
numberplate as the first letter of each
word, for example: TGZ – THERE GOES
ZEPHIR.

I SPY

The first person to spot an agreed object – a black dog, a traffic cone, etc – wins.

BOTTICELLI

One traveller chooses a famous person and tells the others the first
letter of the name. They ask questions, in turn, ('Are you American?'
'Are you dead?') and are given only 'yes' or 'no' answers.
The person who guesses correctly has the next turn.

GAMES

'I WAS GOING INTO THE JUNGLE AND I PACKED MY TRUNK...'

Each player adds something to the list in turn, repeating what has gone before. The last person to repeat the whole list wins. Of course, the objects can be as ridiculous as you like: 'I was going into the jungle, and I packed my trunk and in it I put a sponge bag, a chocolate cake and my pet wart hog…'

SNAP!

Someone names an object everyone can see (a pigeon, a flag, etc). The first person to spot another the same shouts, 'Snap!'

BABAR'S

Make a model of Babar's hot air balloon

WHAT TO DO:

Make some papier mâché. Tear newspaper into strips, put in a bucket and cover with hot water. Leave overnight, then squeeze out any water.

YOU WILL NEED:

plain flour; water; petroleum jelly; scissors

a balloon; an empty margarine tub; newspaper

paper or fine card; poster paint; string; glue

Pour a cup of water into a bowl. Add ¼ to ½ cup of flour and stir to make a thick paste. Mash the wet paper with a little paste. Blow up the balloon and tie.

Smear petroleum jelly all over it and cover with a layer of papier mâché. Leave to dry for 24 hours, then cover with another layer. Pop the balloon with a pin and pull it gently out the papier mâché.

BALLOON

to hang in your room.

Paint the balloon in bright colours. Paint the card/paper the colour of straw and cut into strips. Plait the strips, and glue on to the margarine tub so that it looks like a basket. Make holes round the rim of the tub and thread equal lengths of string through.

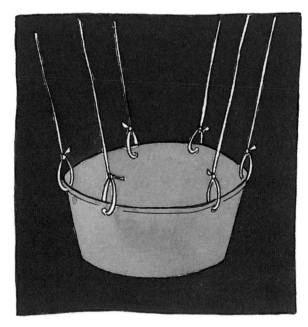

Tie a length of string round the middle of the balloon, glueing in place, and attach the strings from the basket to it. Now you could make a model Babar (see page 11) to put in the basket – or fill it with sweets for a gift.

41

BABAR'S

CELESTE'S PITTA POCKETS

Cut pitta breads open down one side to make a pocket. Stuff with grated cheese, adding chopped onion, slices of tomato or pineapple chunks. Wrap in foil and cook on the barbecue for about five minutes, until the cheese is melted.

CHOCOLATE TUSKS

For each tusk: peel a banana and slice in two lengthwise Put a chocolate flake – or pieces of chocolate – between the banana halves and wrap in foil. Roast on the barbecue for about ten minutes, until the chocolate has melted. Serve with vanilla ice cream.

JUNGLE JUICE

In a large jug, mix 2 cupfuls of fresh orange juice, 3 tbsps blackcurant syrup, 2 tbsps lime cordial and a bottle of fizzy lemonade. Stir to mix and add lizards' eyes: make by plugging the holes in cocktail cherries with a little marzipan, coloured green with food colouring.

BARBECUE

in a clearing in the jungle,
barbecue weather.

VEGETABLE KEBABS

Wash and deseed red, green and yellow peppers and cut into chunks. Thread on to metal skewers, along with cherry tomatoes, mushrooms, baby sweetcorn – whatever combination of vegetables you like. Leave in a sauce of sunflower oil, lemon juice, salt and pepper for an hour or so, and then barbecue for about ten minutes, brushing with the sauce and turning to cook on all sides. Serve with a dip of chilled thick Greek yogurt a squeeze of lemon and some chopped mint.

PARROT PARCELS

Put a slice of peeled pineapple on a square of foil, and top with any of your favourite fruits. Mango is especially good. Add a lemon juice and drizzle on some honey. Seal the parcels well and roast on the barbecue for about ten minutes. When you open them, they will have made their own delicious syrup.

ZEPHIR'S BREEZE

Mix two cups of fresh orange juice with two cups of pineapple juice and a can of coconut milk and chill well.

43

GINGERBREAD

These elephants are delicious. Make lots of them

YOU WILL NEED:
200g (8oz) self-raising flour
1 level tsp salt
2 level tsps powdered ginger
1 level tsp mixed spice
100g (4oz) white cooking fat
75g (3oz) soft brown sugar
3 tbsps cold milk to mix, plus a little extra milk
icing sugar

WHAT TO DO:

Trace round the elephant shape below and cut out. Place your tracing onto card and cut round it to make your elephant biscuit cutter.

Make sure there is a shelf placed just above the centre of the oven. Heat oven to 400°F, 200°C. Grease a baking tray.

Shake the flour, salt, ginger and spice through a sieve into a mixing bowl. Add the fat, and cut it into the dry mixture with a round-topped knife. Then, rub the mixture into the fat with cool fingers until it looks like breadcrumbs.

ELEPHANTS

...and arrange them in a line – tusk to tail.

Add the sugar. Add the milk, mix in with the knife, and gather together with your hand to make a fairly stiff dough. Put on to a surface dusted with flour and shape into a ball. Roll out fairly thinly. Put your cutter on top and cut round it carefully to make elephant shapes. Gather together the trimmings, roll out again and cut more elephants. Make king elephants by cutting a crown on top. Bake in the oven for 15 minutes, or until the elephants are golden brown.

Take tray out of oven with oven gloves. Leave the elephants to stand for 10 minutes before carefully lifting off the tray and on to a wire tray to cool. Mix icing sugar with a few drops of lemon juice or water and decorate as shown below, filling in a tusk and adding eyes to each.

You can make extra-special King Babar elephants by decorating the crowns with edible gold leaf (from craft shops). Stick the gold leaf down with a little egg white.

GUARDIAN

Babar once had a dream about elephants with wings, and bringing happiness to Celesteville.

Here are some winged elephants for you. Write beside them the qualities